This Book Belongs To:

Name: _____

Grade: _____

VOCABULARY
IS ESSENTIAL
KAYLA & KYLE

ISBN: 978-1-7330681-0-9
Library of Congress Control Number: 2020925988
Copyright © 2021 by Mother Hubbard & Co. LLC

Mother Hubbard & Co. LLC
3375 Centerville HWY #391385
Snellville, GA 30039
www.MotherHubbard.us

Dedication

I dedicate this book to my future puppy. I promise to take care of you and give you all the love you'll ever need.

Nicholas B.

KAYLA & KYLE
THE WALKING DICTIONARIES

vol 2

A Puppy Surprise

By Nicholas Buamah
illustrated by Linda H

A Puppy Surprise

Kyle loves puppies. He loves them so much that every year for his birthday, he would petition his parents to surprise him with one.

Every year, his parents would tell him the same thing, "Kyle, we don't think you're ready for the responsibility of a puppy quite yet."

Never giving up hope, Kyle would try to think of new ways to show his parents that he was more responsible than the year before.

Today started off just like any normal school day for Kayla and Kyle. Once Kayla was done preparing herself for school, she took a moment to tidy up her room.

She loves her room to always look immaculate, so she never leaves before making her bed and putting everything away.

Kyle is the antithesis of Kayla. He never tidies up his room before leaving, but he always makes sure that his infamous hat collection stays immaculate.

He's very meticulous about his hats. He even added extra shelves so that he'd have the perfect spot for when he purchased new ones.

After scanning over his hat collection, Kyle of course grabbed his favorite blue one and headed off to school alongside his sister.

While Kayla and Kyle were on their way to school, they noticed a brown cardboard box all alone on a park bench. Kyle immediately read the words written on the box in bold black ink: "FREE PUPPY!"

"Do you see what's written on that box?" Kyle asked his sister, as he stared incredulously.

"Yes, it says Free Puppy!" Kayla replied.

"Do you really think there's a puppy inside?" Kyle asked curiously.

"There's only one way to find out!" said Kayla.

As Kyle moved closer to the bench the top of the box sprang open, and out popped a puppy's head! Kyle was ecstatic when he saw the puppy, and the puppy was so excited to see Kyle that he jumped into his arms and started licking his face.

Kyle knew how his parents felt about him having a puppy, but how could they say no to something so cute?

Kyle had an idea. What better way to show his parents that he's responsible enough for a puppy, than by taking care of one? He decided to take the puppy with him, and off to school they went.

When they arrived at school, Kyle met up with his best friend Nick, the mathematical genius. Nick was thrilled to see the puppy and wanted to know what his name was, but Kyle had been so excited about finding the puppy that he never thought to name him!

"Hmm... What should we call you?" he asked the adorable white ball of fur.

After a few moments of contemplating, Nick said, "How about Snowball?"

Kyle thought the name fit his new puppy perfectly. Now, he just had to figure out how to get through the day without Snowball being seen or heard. He soon found out that it would be easier said than done.

Kyle's first class was gym. He decided to leave Snowball in the boy's locker room until class was over. He wanted Snowball to have enough space to run around and play without being seen by any teachers.

Once gym class was over, Kyle returned to the locker room to find that his new puppy had caused quite a mess! Snowball had pulled everyone's clothes out of their lockers and onto the floor.

He even turned Kyle's favorite hat into a chew toy! Kyle arrived just in time to prevent Snowball from obliterating it completely.

Next, the pair had to make it through math class. Kyle placed his new puppy inside his backpack hoping that Snowball would stay quiet for the next forty-five minutes.

At the start of class, Ms. Morrow asked everyone to turn in their math homework. Kyle reached into his backpack to retrieve his, but found that Snowball had ripped the paper to shreds.

"What happened to your homework, Kyle?" Ms. Morrow asked with a frown.

Kyle replied honestly, "My dog ate it."

The class erupted in laughter because everyone knew that Kyle didn't have a dog.

With only one more class to go before school ended, Kyle decided to leave Snowball in the janitor's closet until the end of the day. He knew that the janitor had already retrieved his cleaning supplies and wouldn't be back until class was over.

"You can't get into too much mischief in here," Kyle said to Snowball. "I'll be back to get you real soon!"

Kyle headed to class, without realizing that he hadn't shut the closet door completely.

After a few minutes of sniffing around in the janitor's closet, Snowball noticed that the door was left slightly cracked.

He used his head to push the door open and proceeded to stroll down the school's desolate hallway.

Every door that Snowball passed was closed, but at the very end of the hallway he found one that was wide open! The little puppy's eyes grew wide with excitement, and he darted right inside the room.

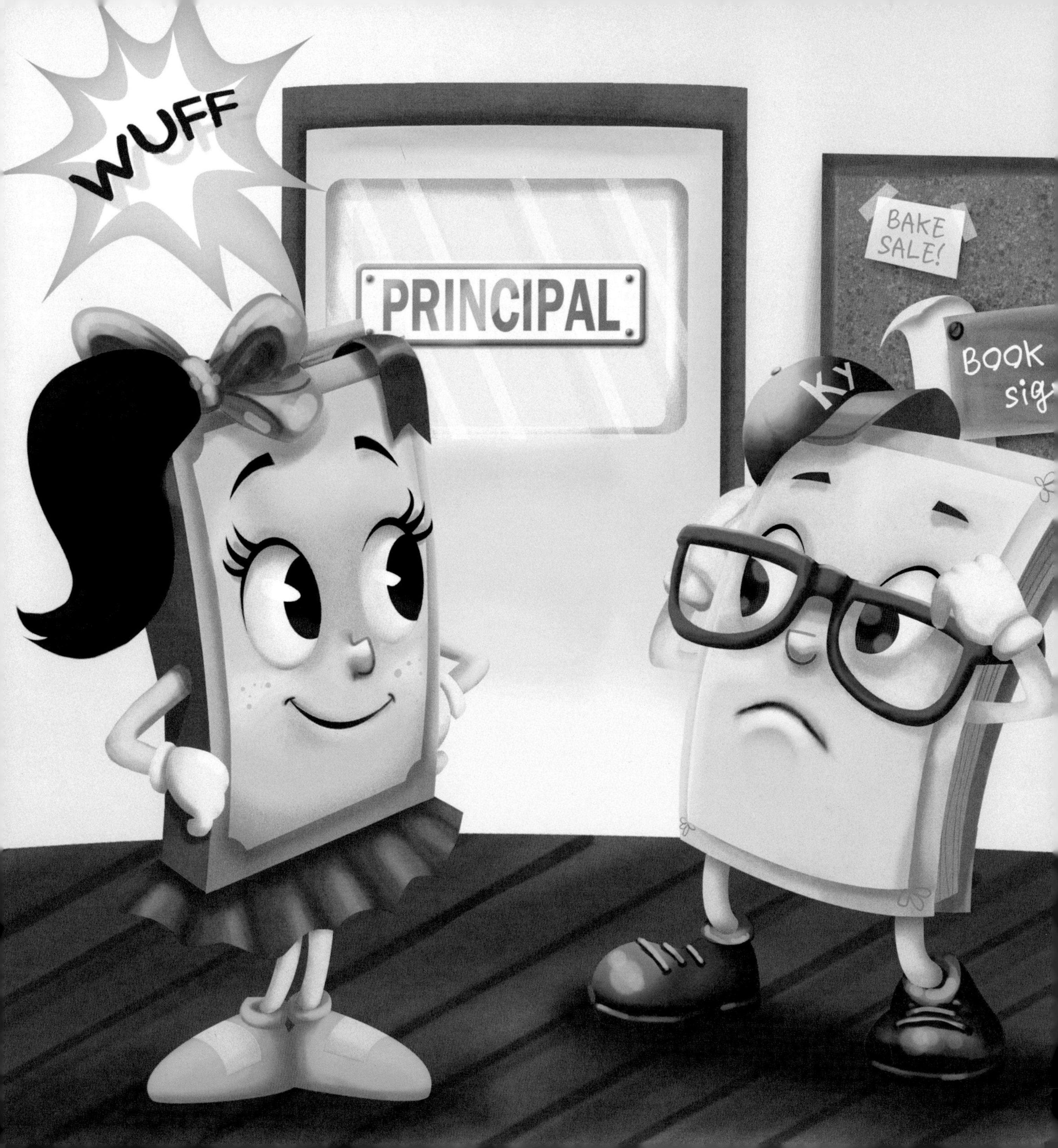
WUFF
PRINCIPAL
BAKE SALE!
BOOK
KY

As soon as the school bell rang, Kyle immediately ran to the janitor's closet to retrieve Snowball. The closet door was open, but there was no sign of his fluffy white puppy anywhere.

Kyle was distraught. He was worried that his new puppy had run away. Kayla volunteered to help Kyle find Snowball.

After several minutes of searching, Kyle heard a small bark coming from Principal Swift's office.

The kids slowly peeked inside the principal's office and found that Snowball had completely destroyed the room.

The papers from Principal Swift's desk were now scattered all over the floor. The lamp was lying on its side, and Principal Swift's coffee cup had been flipped over, spilling coffee everywhere.

At that moment, Kyle realized that his parents had been prudent after all. He was definitely not ready for the responsibility that comes with caring for a puppy.

In the middle of all this mess, the strangest thing happened. Principal Swift walked into his office, and a smile stretched across his face. "Well, what do we have here?" he asked.

He wasn't at all upset that the puppy had wrecked his office. "Isn't he the cutest thing?" Principal Swift asked, as he picked up the puppy.

At that very moment, Kyle had an epiphany. He would offer to let Principal Swift keep Snowball as a pet.

Kyle explained to Principal Swift that he found Snowball at the park alone inside a box, and that he'd been trying to hide the puppy at school all day.

After hearing his story, Principal Swift was enamored and happily accepted Kyle's offer.

Today turned out to be a phenomenal day for both Kayla and Kyle.

The End!

GLOSSARY

Antithesis:	Direct opposite
Contemplate:	To think about carefully
Desolate:	Empty
Distraught:	Deeply upset

Ecstatic:	Joyful and excited
Enamored:	Filled with love
Epiphany:	A sudden realization
Erupt:	To explode

Immaculate:	Clean and tidy
Incredulous:	Unable to believe it
Infamous:	Having a bad reputation
Meticulous:	Attentive to detail

Mischief:	Playful misbehavior
Obliterate:	To completely destroy
Petition:	To ask
Prudent:	Wise and practical

Nicholas Buamah

Born in Atlanta, GA, Nicholas Buamah couldn't be happier to share his love of vocabulary and storytelling with other kids.

By the age of 10, he's published two books and founded the nonprofit group Books Without Borders, Inc. to help supply underprivileged communities with books and school supplies. He has made several TV and radio appearances and has received many accolades for his literary accomplishments from both celebrities and political officials.

In addition to excelling academically and as a writer, Nicholas also has a love for sports and activities such as basketball, golf and playing chess. He will be releasing two more books before the end of this year that you're sure to enjoy.

Nicholas' future plan is to study at the Massachusetts Institute of Technology (MIT) to become a mechanical engineer when he gets older. In the meantime, he plans to keep spreading the joy of reading to the world.

VETERINARY TIPS FOR YOUR NEW PUPPY

CONGRATULATIONS ON YOUR NEW PUPPY! FOLLOW THESE TIPS SO THAT YOUR PUPPY WILL BE HEALTHY AND HAPPY FOR A VERY LONG TIME!

Housing Needs

- ✓ **Puppy Food** – A balanced puppy specific diet is needed to help your puppy grow
  - • Training Treats – Small chewable chews are tasty and help to create positive reinforcements while training.
- ✓ **Food dishes** – Separate water and food dishes will be needed. Metal or ceramic material is easy to clean. Plastic can harbor bacteria and create infections.
- ✓ **Bedding** – A soft bed and warm area like a small crate are best to keep your puppy warm and safe. Do not allow your puppy to explore when you are not home. Puppies can injure themselves if not watched.
- ✓ **Potty Pads** – These training tools will help to teach your puppy the proper place to go potty. Clean and remove dirty pads often.
- ✓ **Toys** – Puppies like to chew things! Provide toys that are safe to chew and provide playful stimulation for your growing puppy.

Veterinary Needs

- ✓ **Veterinary Check-Up** – Take your puppy to the Veterinarian when you adopt them. The doctor will check your puppy and plan a schedule to vaccinate, deworm, and provide any other medical needs.
- ✓ **Flea, Tick and Heart worm prevention** – Your Veterinarian will give your puppy a product that will protect them from internal and external parasites.

Training Needs

✓ **Obedience Training** – Whether you train personally or use a professional, it's important to set boundaries with your puppy. Training helps to keep your puppy safe and prevent damage to your home or others.
  • Play Biting – Puppies like to bite and although they don't mean to, this can be painful. Discourage this behavior by redirecting your puppy's attention to acceptable toys and chewable treats.
✓ **Potty Training** – Consistency is the key. Puppies need to potty often, so take your puppy for a walk three to four times a day to allow them to potty. Give training treats for positive reinforcement. Most puppies will be potty trained between 6-8 months!

Most importantly provide lots of LOVE! Kisses, hugs and tail wags are the secret ingredient to a long, healthy relationship with your new puppy!!

Director of Veterinary Inclusion and Diversity Programs of VCA Hospitals, Dr. Timbrala Marshall.

Thank you for these helpful veterinary tips.

Dr. Timbrala Marshall has worked as a veterinarian in the Atlanta area for over 10 years. She is currently the director of veterinary equity inclusion and diversity programs for VCA Hospitals. In this role, she focuses on creating and nurturing relationships with Historically Black Colleges and Universities (HBCUs), Hispanic Serving Institutions (HSIs), among other academic institutions. She also helps to build and lead programs to reach and support underserved communities.

For more information about VCA Hospitals visit:
www.VCAHospitals.com

Dr. Timbrala Marshall

Share your heart for animals in need

atlanta hu♥ane society

Adopting an Animal who is in a Foster Home

1. **Start on our adoptable animals' website pages.**
2. **Read their biographies!** Each animal has a personalized biography that talks about their likes and dislikes and will help you learn a bit more about them and decide if they'd be a good match for you.
3. **Apply to adopt.** Once you've found an animal who is a good match, fill out a pre-adoption application form at atlantahumane.org/adoption-application
4. **We'll be in touch.** When your application is received, we'll be in contact within 48-72 via email to let you know that you've been placed in a queue for the animal or via phone to schedule a meet and greet.
5. **Meet your new best friend!** Our team will set up a socially-distanced meet and greet with you and the pet and will be there to answer any other questions you might have.
6. **Finalize the adoption.** If you're ready to adopt, our adoption counselors will process your adoption and adoption fee virtually. Our adoption fees are cashless and touchless. You will be asked to submit your adoption fee via a secured payment processing link located on our website. We accept all major credit and debit cards.
7. **Take home your new friend.** Once this virtual adoption process is complete, you're all set and ready to start a new journey with your best friend.

   We're here for you post-adoption. Even after your adoption is completed, we'll be here for you if you have questions about being a pet owner for years to come. Especially in these times, understanding your pet's health and behavior can be difficult, so don't hesitate to set up a free virtual veterinary assistance or free virtual behavior assistance session with one of our team members.

In-shelter adoption also available

Adopt A Loyal Friend Today!

Your best friend is waiting for you!

www.AtlantaHumane.org

Made in the USA
Monee, IL
17 May 2022

96608195R00029